Should I Speak Up?

Written by
OLIVIA & RINNAH MADUABUCHI

Illustrated by
ABIDI & SOLATI

This book is dedicated to all kids, encouraging them to speak up for themselves and others too. Let's speak up friends and save people from hurt and abuse. Big thanks to Aunty Jo for guiding us through this project and to our entire family and friends for making this book a reality. We love you all!

Should I Speak-Up?
1st Edition

Published in the United States
Audience: age 4-8

Should I Speak Up?

Written by
OLIVIA & RINNAH MADUABUCHI

Illustrated by
ABIDI & SOLATI

My name is Zinny, and I like to mind my own business. I'd rather not get into other people's problems even when someone is mistreated. I guess you can say, I don't like to speak up so I don't get beat up.

At home, Mom and Dad always say,
"Mind your business Zinny!" So, I thought
that applied to everything else.

I've seen kids get pushed around by older kids.
I thought to myself, if they don't like it,
they should tell a grown up.

One time, I saw a little boy being pushed around and called mean names by a group of kids. His friend tried to help but was beaten up too. That scared me really bad, and I decided even more not to meddle in people's business. Hmmm, was I wrong?

A few days later, I saw my best friend, Chloe, being mistreated by some bigger kids. They teased her, pushed her, took her snack, and threw her backpack to the ground. Chloe picked up her backpack without saying a word and walked into the bathroom. So I followed her to the bathroom to talk to her, there she was crying.

"Why do you let them treat you that way Chloe?" I questioned.
"They threatened to beat me up if I told anyone," She answered.
She pleaded for me not to tell anyone.
I wondered if that was why the other kids kept quiet too.

When I got home that day, I was and looked very sad and concerned for Chloe. My big sister, Zettie, asked me what was wrong over and over again until I couldn't hold it in anymore.

"Chloe is mistreated at school," I whispered.
"By who?" Zettie questioned.
"By some bigger kids." I replied.
"Why doesn't she tell anyone?" Zettie asked.
"She's afraid because they told her they'll beat her up if she tells anyone." I answered.
"You should tell this to a grown up like our parents or a teacher.
They'll know what to do." Zettie suggested.

"I feel like I've betrayed her by telling you." I continued.
"What do you mean?" Zettie responded.
I'm not supposed to tell anyone at all.
I pinkie promised." I sadly replied.
"I once had someone in my class who was always treated bad by some group of mean kids. " Zettie proceeded.

"What did she do?" I questioned.
"She got really sad and almost hurt herself,
but her parents found out and got her help on
time." Zettie continued.
"I'm scared. I better tell a grown up so they
can help her before she injures herself."
I mumbled tearing.
"I think that is a good idea." Zettie muttered,
hugging me.

The next time I saw Chloe being bullied,
I knew exactly what to do. I went straight to
my teacher and told her what happened,
everything I saw, and everything Chloe told me.

My teacher told me she was very proud of me for speaking up. She immediately reported the mean big kids to the principal who summoned them and their parents for a conference.

After the meeting, the mean kids had
to go to Chloe to apologize for their bad behavior
and harsh words to her. Chloe said, "I forgive you!"
They were suspended from school and their parents
also punished them at home for being such bullies.
They never mistreated anyone after they returned
to school or at least we never saw them do that again.

The next day during recess, Chloe gave me
a hug and thanked me for standing
up for her. She promised to speak up
for herself and others too and does that now.
I am very happy for her because she isn't getting
mistreated or oppressed anymore. I am also
proud of myself for speaking up.

Now I know when to speak up and when to mind my own business.
Next time you see someone being mistreated, remember to say something; tell a grown up, like a parent or a teacher.

So join me friends, let us speak up and put bullies out of business. Speak Up! It's the right thing to do. When you see something, say something.

Question Time?

1. Do you speak up when you see something wrong? Why or Why not?

2. What would you do if someone mistreats you or a friend and commands you not to tell anyone?

3. What does it mean to you to speak up?

Anti Bullying Pledge Certificate

I,..., pledge to speak up for myself and others, to be kind to other people and care about them. So help me God.

Sign:...............................

Date:...............................

Speak Up Squad

(Here you get to add the names of those on your speak up squad)

Speak Up Stickers

Speak Up Stickers

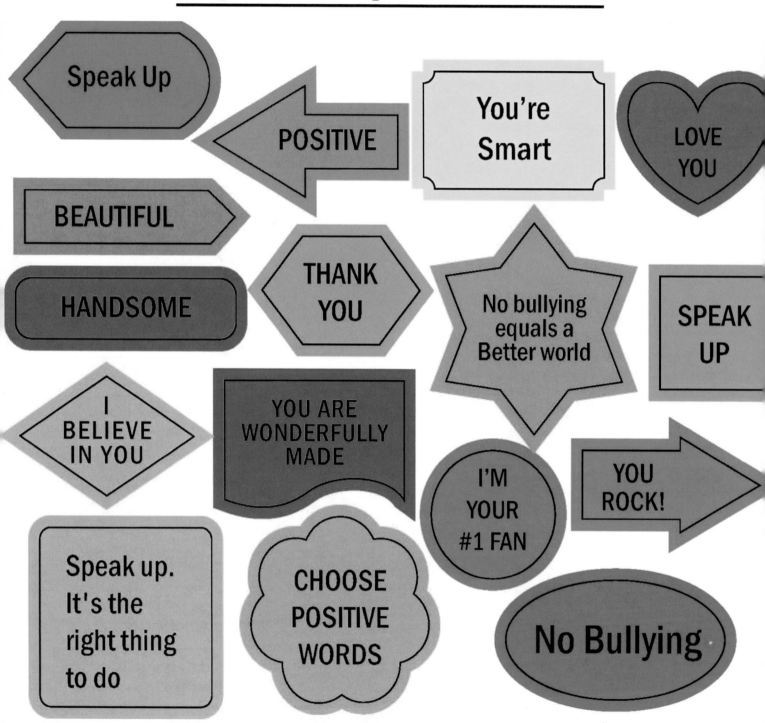

List of other books by Authors

1. Must I wash my hands!?

Coming Soon

2. Should I brush my teeth?

3. Should I clean my room?

4. Zinny's book of opposites.

Little Zinny loves to mind her business. One day, she sees her best friend getting mistreated. Let's find out what Zinny learns in this simple but powerful story.

About The Authors

Olivia is a 10 year old who loves to read, write, and be a caring big sister. She enjoyed writing every part of this book and hopes to do more in the the future. ;)

Rinnah is an 8 year old who enjoys making and learning about origami. She loves to read and be a team player. She enjoyed making this book alongside her big sister. :)

Made in the USA
Monee, IL
24 January 2022

89740310R00017